MATTHEW WILLIAMSON

Fashion, Print & Colouring Book

Laurence King Publishing

Twenty years ago I set up my fashion company, and so I wanted to mark this occasion by creating something personal yet also something to be shared and enjoyed. This book felt like a passion project for me to mark this important milestone.

Colour, pattern and print are and always have been at the heart of my work and so this book centres on these aspects, with prints I've personally chosen to reflect the DNA of my brand.

This book is for everyone to enjoy – young or not so young, novice or talented artist – and to experience some of the prints I've created over the years, and most importantly, to share the process and journey of how each one came to life.

You will find imagery that inspired each print, me at work painting in the studio, drawing and creating the first stages of the print, right up to the finished garment or other products the print was then used for. Black-and-white renders have been created so you can have a go yourself and recreate your own version, be it a direct copy of the original or your own unique interpretation.

Whether you use this simply for inspiration from time to time or you dive straight in, start colouring and make the book your own, I hope you enjoy it as much as I have enjoyed creating it.

Thank you to all my talented staff, past and present, who have contributed and played a huge part in helping bring these prints to life.

Happy colouring!

Matthew x

This book is dedicated to Skye.

DRAGONFLY
DANCE

'Dragonflies have always fascinated me. I'm drawn to the iridescent, stained-glass beauty of their wings.'

My first collection in 1997 was called 'Electric Angels' and was an ode to these amazing creatures. There wasn't actually any print in this first show – instead I had hand-embroidered organza dragonfly wings across shift dresses or sitting on the shoulders of cardigans in contrasting pops of tangerine, magenta and aqua.

My dragonfly print appeared on the runway in Spring/Summer 2014 – fragile wings swirling across chiffon gowns. The print featured opposite was a more precise, simplistic repeat pattern that I first used in 2004, where I drew a fine black outline to frame the jewel-like colours in the wings. Now it's your turn to colour in my 'Dragonfly Dance'.

BUTTERFLY
WHEEL

'I like to think this print embodies the DNA of my brand: feminine, exotic, delicate and rich in detail.'

I've done many prints, embroideries and textile designs featuring butterflies over the years, but this print remains one of my all-time favourites. I used this version, 'Butterfly Wheel', in my Spring/Summer 2008 catwalk collection, printed on ruffles of chiffon and lace-panelled dresses, as I wanted to capture the fluttering delicacy of their wings within each design.

I am forever snapping photos of butterflies when I see them, and on my travels I always look out for the patterns on their wings and the shapes they form. They inspire a lot of my work, from fashion to interiors, stationery to furniture.

PINEAPPLE
PAISLEY

'I love the spiky symmetry of this tropical fruit, and its suggestion of high summer.'

The pineapple has a natural architectural beauty, and I used its shape to inspire this botanical 'Pineapple Paisley' print in a repeated arrangement. I wanted to retain a painterly, almost naïve quality to the pattern, so we set about hand-painting each element in the studio before creating the layout.

So far this print has not appeared on the catwalk, but it has been used on kaftans and beachwear, and can be seen at its best on my wallpaper collection that hangs on the walls in my studio in London, adding a touch of tropical sunshine. I think this print represents what we do, and hope it endures and becomes a timeless classic!

RAJ
PATCHWORK

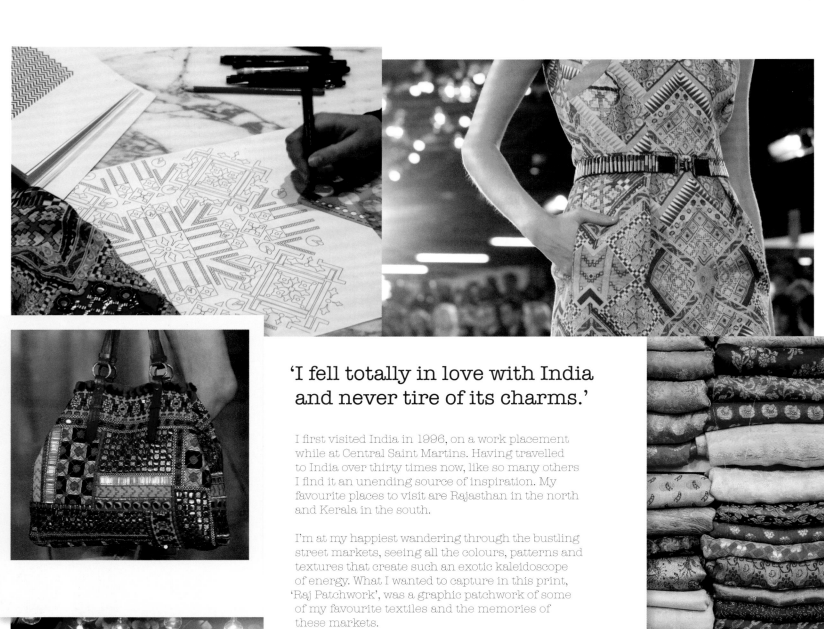

'I fell totally in love with India and never tire of its charms.'

I first visited India in 1996, on a work placement while at Central Saint Martins. Having travelled to India over thirty times now, like so many others I find it an unending source of inspiration. My favourite places to visit are Rajasthan in the north and Kerala in the south.

I'm at my happiest wandering through the bustling street markets, seeing all the colours, patterns and textures that create such an exotic kaleidoscope of energy. What I wanted to capture in this print, 'Raj Patchwork', was a graphic patchwork of some of my favourite textiles and the memories of these markets.

This print was used across many garments, in many different ways, in my 2013 collection and it became the basis for my 'Indian Summer' show.

QUEPOS
PARROTS

'I love parrots' majestic beauty,
their rainbow-like wingspan
and electric colour palette.'

My most recent sighting was earlier this year in
Quepos, Costa Rica, when a pair of macaws swooped
over the jungle canopy outside my bedroom like
darting red arrows in perfect unison. Parrots often
find their way into my work, from the catwalk to a silk
printed scarf, to shimmering wallpaper and interiors.

The print featured here was originally done as a
screenprint in 2003. At the time, we were very
limited as to the amount of screens we could afford
to create it, but restrictions can often be inspiring
and its stencil-like quality retains a certain charm.

More recently we've created a painterly parrot in
the studio in tones of aqua, mint, jade and purple,
then printed it on to silk chiffon.

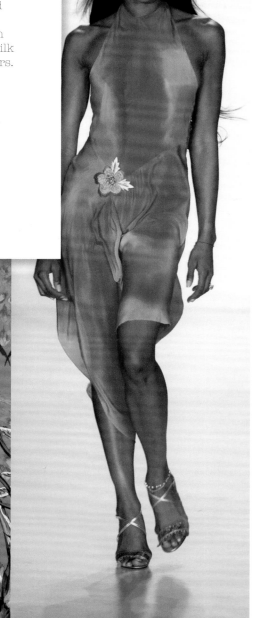

LEOPARDO

'When I want a print to feel powerful, dynamic and full of energy I choose the leopard.'

My work is often associated with the softer side of femininity so it's nice sometimes to try something different and show another dimension. The slinky black silk jersey set the tone, and I wanted to keep the colours dark, rich and intense for this nocturnal design. This print is for the femme fatale, the life and soul of the party who dances till dawn.

I love the spirit of this print and adapted it to create a wallpaper design with the leopards stalking between metallic peacock tail feathers and foliage. It's bold and striking, and makes equal impact on a slinky silk dress or a bedroom wall, so now it's your turn to colour on the wild side!

FLAMINGO
CLUB

'I'm in my element designing for the summer months and this print is just that: jet set, tropical and escapist.'

I first drew this flamingo print in pencil, then painted the palms and orchids to create a patchwork of paradise.

The 'Flamingo Club' print has stayed true to its holiday spirit. It has appeared on swimwear and kaftans for my beachwear line, and has become one of my favourite wallpapers – currently hanging on the walls in my showroom dressing room. It's such a happy backdrop for meetings and customers alike, and always brings a smile to people's faces. Create your own sunshine by adding colour!

MOTHER
AMAZON

'Trips to Bali, Costa Rica and Mexico are such rich sources of inspiration for me.'

'Mother Amazon' is one of my most recent prints, a complex collage bursting with life and tropical elements. Travel has always been my greatest indulgence, and there are still so many new and beautiful places I want to discover, as well as revisiting my old favourites.

By painting snakes, butterflies and flowers separately in the studio, I was then able to build the layers of this print. I arranged all these elements around hearts encased in circles, creating focal points. This print has been used on hammered silk summer separates, and has now expanded into my interiors collection.

ENGLISH
GARDEN

'I like to think of this print as my version of a quintessential English garden.'

While inspiration can often come from my travels and warmer climes, I'm equally drawn to things closer to home. This print takes inspiration from oriental design, and is essentially a nostalgic view of birds in flight or perched on peony branches.

I used the print in my Autumn/Winter 2006 collection on silk chiffon gowns, and chose a duck-egg blue wash to evoke a feeling of faded grandeur. It was designed to have an almost vintage quality.

I am only a novice gardener but the more time I spend in the garden the more I am attracted to flowers and plants I can recognize and grow myself. I am sure they will find their way into future prints, but until then bring your own colour to this 'English Garden'.

JARDIN
MAJORELLE

'I'm always intoxicated by the sun-bleached, spicy colours of Marrakesh.'

I've visited Morocco many times over the years, the first in 1996 with my mum as her birthday gift, and I always find ideas there. The architecture, interiors, street life and souks are a heady mix, full of handmade tin lamps and graphic woven textiles.

I wanted to capture all these elements in one print, and created an almost tile-like base reminiscent of the ceramics I saw in the souks. Then I overlaid the print with painterly crocus flowers to give contrast and depth.

The hot-house colours came from my visit to the iconic Jardin Majorelle, where tones of lavender, terracotta and Klein Blue sit in perfect harmony.

WOODLAND
PICNIC

'For this print, I simply shut my eyes and imagined my dream woodland picnic right here at home.'

As I was working on this print I hosted a picnic party in my back garden and set about incorporating all the elements you see here: strawberries, cocktails, flora and fauna, even fake palm trees and parrots. A magical secret summer party ensued and I always remember that evening when I see 'Woodland Picnic'.

I have always loved the English countryside. In London I live between Regent's Park and Hampstead Heath, and this print pulled together different elements of nature, both close to home and with a touch of the tropical. I love the busy composition of this print – just how a picnic should be. For a contrast, I cut it into simple classic cocktail dresses for the party season.

SUNBIRD

'The sunbird darts in and out of the graphic angles and symmetry of the palm leaves.'

Whenever I see palm trees, I remember painting them on a trip to the Maldives and witnessing a beautiful sunset in the Bahamas. I have many happy memories associated with them.

I wanted to capture this feeling in the print, where tiny sunbirds and palm leaves appear on a light, white muslin. It first appeared in 2004 on kaftans and swimwear in a summer collection, and it has since been applied to wallpaper.

I often see a natural progression from fashion to home, and this print is a good example of how one idea and pattern can have many uses.

HERITAGE
BUTTERFLY

'I have a wall at home in my hallway covered in butterfly memorabilia.'

Pictures, postcards, plates and paintings mostly collected on my travels adorn every inch of the wall, and friends and family always know I can never have enough butterflies, so birthday presents for me are quite easy!

Orchids are one of my favourite flowers and the butterfly has been a constant source of inspiration throughout my career, so it made sense to combine the two.

This print was first used on a silk square where the butterfly takes centre stage, and I liked it so much that I reinvented it to create a one-shoulder summer dress. I like colours to be bold yet wearable, like my Spring/Summer 2002 butterfly dress. Choose hot tones for the flowers and butterfly, and a cool, more calming lemon for the 'ground' colour.

TALITHA
PATCHWORK

'I grew up in Manchester surrounded by prints, patterns and colour.'

My mother loved to dress up and express herself through her clothes. Her sense of style made me realize the power of colour and pattern, and how both could lift the spirits, ultimately inspiring me to follow fashion as a career.

As a child growing up in the 1970s, I was drawn to bohemian British designers: Ossie Clark, Biba, Celia Birtwell and Zandra Rhodes, all masters of pattern and print. This design inspired by style icon Talitha Getty was part of my Spring/Summer 2007 collection and reminds me of that period when florals and graphic prints elegantly clashed together.

PEACOCK
HEARTS

'I love the bold graphic simplicity of this print, which somehow also retains a feminine quality.'

Peacocks featured back in my first show, 'Electric Angels', as embroidery, but it wasn't until 2004 that I first designed and printed them on to chiffon. We made one of our most popular dresses with this print. My good friend Sienna Miller fell in love with this dress and from then on I've always considered her a muse.

I'm drawn to the peacock's symmetrical plumes, ornate detail and sumptuous colourings. This print has seen many reincarnations over the years. 'Peacock Hearts' has been made into a rug, printed in shades of electric blue on wallpaper, and has even inspired jewellery.

MERIDA
STARS

'I first went to Ibiza to visit my friend Jade Jagger who had a house on the island.'

I was taken by her style, her home and her bohemian way of life, which seemed so idyllic. My friendship with Jade helped shape my first few collections. To many, my clothes became associated with the Ibiza jet set lifestyle.

This print appeared on the catwalk in 2009. I wanted to capture the essence of all night parties, hedonism and a youthful energy. I love its psychedelic, hippy, rainbow vibe. Whether you see stars or fireworks, graffiti or sea urchins, colour pigments or simply the spirit of joy - this print has no real start or end.

Dragonfly Dance
Opener: © Susan Leggett/Dreamstime.com
Process page: top left © Catwalking.com;
top middle © Catwalking.com; centre right
Dragonfly Dance Wallpaper from Matthew Williamson
at Osborne & Little; bottom right © James D. Kelly
Final image: © Catwalking.com
Drawing: Pentagram

Butterfly Wheel
Opener: © Eric Raptosh Photography/
Blend Images LLC/Getty Images
Process page: bottom right © Duresta photographed
by Simon Bevan ; bottom left © Catwalking.com;
centre left © Super Prin/shutterstock.com
Final image: © Catwalking.com
Drawing: Mariona Alegre Freixa

Pineapple Paisley
Opener: © www.bridgemanart.com
Process page: centre right © Holly Falconer; bottom
right © Rhys Frampton; bottom left © James D. Kelly
Drawing: Mariona Alegre Freixa

Raj Patchwork
Opener: © Simon Bracken/DK Images
Process page: centre right © Donald Iain Smith/
Blend Images/Corbis; bottom right © Kayt Jones/
Art + Commerce
Drawing: Pentagram

Quepos Parrots
Opener: © Jim Zuckerman/Corbis
Process page: top left © Rhys Frampton/Kate B,
Next models; bottom right © Catwalking.com
Final image: © Catwalking.com
Drawing: Mariona Alegre Freixa

Leopardo
Opener: © Dinodia/Corbis
Process page: top right image courtesy of
Holly Falconer shot for Toni & Guy Products;
bottom right Rhys Frampton/Grace Elizabeth,
Next models; bottom left Leopardo Wallpaper
from Matthew Williamson at Osborne & Little
Final image: © Catwalking.com
Drawing: Mariona Alegre Freixa

Flamingo Club
Opener: © Antonio Nunes
Process page: top right © Eddie Wrey/Nimue
Smit, Next models; bottom right © Mitchell Sams;
bottom left Flamingo Club Wallpaper from
Matthew Williamson at Osborne & Little
Drawing: Pentagram and Mariona Alegre Freixa

Mother Amazon
Opener: © Thinkstock
Process page: bottom right © Rhys Frampton/
Kate B, Next models
Final image: © Rhys Frampton/Kate B,
Next models
Drawing: Mariona Alegre Freixa

English Garden
Opener: © Elena Schweitzer/Dreamstime.com
Process page: top left © Suki Dhanda; top right
© www.bridgemanart.com; bottom left
© Catwalking.com
Final image: © Catwalking.com
Drawing: Mariona Alegre Freixa

Jardin Majorelle
Opener: © Cultura RM/Alamy
Process page: top right © Eddie Wrey/Esther
Heesch, Next models
Final image: © Eddie Wrey/Esther
Heesch, Next models
Drawing: Mariona Alegre Freixa

Woodland Picnic
Opener: © Nickolay Khoroshkov/Alamy
Stock Photo
Process page: bottom right © Tommy Clarke/
Agne Konciute, Next models
Final image: © Tommy Clarke/Agne Konciute,
Next models
Drawing: Mariona Alegre Freixa

Sunbird
Opener: © Frederick Mark Sheridan-Johnson/
Alamy Stock Photo
Process page: bottom left © Holly Falconer
Drawing: Mariona Alegre Freixa

Heritage Butterfly
Opener: © Glow Images
Process page: top right © Catwalking.com;
bottom left © Glow Images
Final image: © Rhys Frampton/Kate B,
Next models
Drawing: Mariona Alegre Freixa

Talitha Patchwork
Opener: © Patrick Lichfield/Getty Images
Process page: top right © Image Source/
Getty Images; centre right © David Nyanzi;
bottom left © Catwalking.com
Final image: © Catwalking.com
Drawing: Mariona Alegre Freixa

Peacock Hearts
Opener: © Darren Garrich
Process page: top left: © Catwalking.com;
bottom right courtesy of the Rug Company;
bottom centre: © Catwalking.com; bottom left
© Holly Falconer
Final image: © Catwalking.com
Drawing: Mariona Alegre Freixa

Merida Stars
Opener: © Jamen Percy/Dreamstime.com
Process page: top right © Catwalking.com;
centre right © Mark Milan/Film Magin/
Getty Images; bottom right © Ingrid Rasmussen,
artwork by Rob & Nick Carter
Final image: © Catwalking.com
Drawing: Mariona Alegre Freixa and Charlie Bolton

Cover created by Ellie Vandoorne

Published in 2016 by
Laurence King Publishing Ltd
361-373 City Road, London,
EC1V 1LR, United Kingdom
T + 44 (0)20 7841 6900
F + 44 (0)20 7841 6910
enquiries@laurenceking.com
www.laurenceking.com

A catalogue record for this book is available from
the British Library

ISBN: 978-1-78067-897-9

Design by Charlie Bolton

Printed in China